SHADOW DANCING

First edition. December 2, 2023.

Copyright © 2023 Paul du Buf.

ISBN: 979-8223517702

Written by Paul du Buf.

Table of Contents

SHADOW DANCING

EMBODIED RECOVERY
FROM
TRAUMA AND ADDICTION

Special thanks to Therese for her love and support, my family, friends, and the inspiring and big-hearted colleagues I worked with over the years. And especially the clients I had the privilege of working with.

Introduction

Clients I worked with over the years taught me what was evident from the start but which I didn't acknowledge or recognise then. Thanks to becoming more experienced, my eyes and mind slowly started to discern essential distinctions I will discuss in the coming chapters.

It took me many years to realise and see clients staying trapped in addiction and specifically being informed about one adolescent client who overdosed despite my best efforts to prevent that from happening, to learn there was something essential we were missing, that there was something that I was missing. Although we offer clients with a drug dependency harm minimisation, which also includes a product (Naloxone) that can counteract an opiate overdose, or for people with an alcohol dependency an alcohol detox, a significant number of clients would continue to drink or use opiates without feeling there is an accessible and good alternative and continue their addictive lifestyle. Clients said they could feel debilitated by anxiety and depression, even when prescribed the most minor amounts of opiate replacement medication, and many were hesitant to consider becoming abstinent from all drugs. A colleague now working in a drug community service and who left his opiate dependency in the past told me he still didn't trust himself and would rather not win the lottery as he couldn't predict what he might be tempted to do with his winnings.

This made me reflect and inquire into why I chose to work as an addiction nurse and the role and function of what I call "shadow" that prevents people who battle their dependency or addiction from breaking free. What are those obstacles, and what is the process that drives a shadow forward to become acknowledged, felt, heard and integrated?

Another reason I wrote this book is to celebrate the people who were helped and felt supported by addiction workers and addiction treatment. I estimate that currently, around 10% of people with an addiction severe enough to enter an addiction treatment service will outgrow their dependency on their drug of choice (or addictive behaviour like gambling). By outgrowing, I mean moving on and developing skills that give them options and a way to relate differently to their vulnerability expressed through their particular dependent behaviour.

The current paradigm focuses mainly on harm reduction and recovery rather than healing. New developments and perspectives I discuss in this book, like Internal Family Systems (IFS), Polyvagal Theory (PVT), Somatic Therapies, and Trauma-informed approaches, can increase the chances - when implemented sufficiently in systems and organisations - to support healing.

Most clients I worked with have improved their quality of life greatly through developing and stabilising more practical skills and have benefitted from the harm-reduction effects of treatment.

I use the term "clients" to describe the people that I worked with over the years in my role as a nurse in addiction services as I have never been comfortable calling them patients, which for me has a reference to a more medical setting which, generally speaking, includes an unequal relational power dynamic.

I will use the term "addiction services" to include all regular services that support people with addiction problems, i.e. addiction community services, in-patient detox/rehab services, addiction support services in hospitals, holding cells in police stations and prisons.

The book is called Shadow Dancing, so what do I mean by "shadow" and "dancing"?

I use shadow to refer to that part in us that is not appreciated, repressed, or welcomed into our awareness as we do not consider that part or feel that that part has desirable traits.

It might be a nagging feeling, a feeling of dis-ease about past experiences, something we feel ashamed about or guilty about, or even disgusted. As I use it, "shadow" generally refers to our closet's proverbial skeleton(s), which we don't like to acknowledge or share.

I use dancing as a metaphor to invite qualities and skills that allow us to connect with our shadow parts. Some qualities and skills like a willingness to connect, learn about our shadow part, or a motivation to become more whole (including all parts).

Also, dancing points to a quality of lightness and relaxation, essential as we don't want to dissolve, kill or defeat our shadow but instead focus on a natural integration towards connection, learning, and inclusion.

Shadow can also occur when we idolise people we look up to, meet and relate to, including role models and peers we admire. Who influence our culture, upbringing, morals, and world perception. In our development, when we put these role models on a pedestal, we can create a "golden shadow".

A golden shadow is a part of us that feels inadequate compared to others who show traits or qualities we feel are lacking in ourselves. We might feel disconnected from the positive attributes we see in others and imagine them beyond our abilities.

On the other hand, there are feelings that we become aware of in the face of challenging situations, for example, homelessness, war, famine, violence, hatred ... challenging experiences that can bring difficult emotions to the foreground, which might get us in contact with parts in us that experience vulnerability, sensitivity, awareness of our mortality and anticipated possible physical and mental decline the older we grow.

In contrast to these qualities of vulnerability, some parts can be considered our mindset of achievement and success, celebrated in the Western world. This mindset is primarily interested in what can take us forward, what helps us grow, and what makes us rich, independent, wealthy, famous, respected, admired, etc.

This mindset, focused on our world outside ourselves, generally is focused on creating benefits primarily for ourselves with little interest in qualities like compassion, reflection, stillness, grounding, sensitivity, spaciousness, awareness, mindfulness, and connection.

The concept of shadow - first spoken about by Carl Jung in 1935 - points to a dynamic that occurs to people in different ways and at different times in reaction to any overwhelming, intense event, as our nervous systems are uniquely wired, and some are more easily overwhelmed than others.

Internal Family Systems (IFS), which is a psychotherapeutic model, in their Glossary of Terms (https://ifs-institute.com/resources/research/ifs-glossary-terms), calls the shadow "exiles" and describes them as "parts that have been sequestered within a system for their protection or the protection of the system from them."

Processing those experiences ("exiles") can quickly feel "too much" when we don't titrate or use pendulation (gradual exposure) in the process of reconnecting with them. Our culture and environment generally do not value change over the status quo or respect our struggles and do not want to accept, support, or give exiles attention.

The parts that deal with the "exiles" are called "protectors" by IFS. Protectors can be Firefighters, which IFS defines as "parts that go into action after the exiles have been activated to calm the exiles or distract the system from them (dissociation)", or Managers: "parts that try to run a system in ways that minimise the activation of exiles".

IFS considers parts as pseudo-identities with a history and a specific world perspective. My perspective is they represent a fixed role linked with an over-identification to a narrative and have a job and a function to fulfil at a specific time in our lives. Addictive behaviour can be considered behaviour motivated by a firefighter.

We can benefit getting curious about the information the unconscious, unvalued parts contain and making them conscious. We can communicate with and explore the different fixed parts in us rather than denying the multi-dimensional nature of our being, which has many different perspectives in our inner world that motivate and inform us.

It is about getting curious about why these parts/ perspectives came into existence in the first place, assuming a positive intention and working to allow those parts to feel valuable, welcome and appreciated so they can relax and connect. So we become more whole.

Using the metaphor of shadow dancing points to the intention and opportunity to make contact and re-establish, reconnect with our shadow, realise it is there, acknowledge it, get to know it and learn from what it teaches us.

One of the essential elements necessary in this context is safety. A sense of safety creates a condition for parts we want to get to know better to show themself. This sense of security is linked not so much with our cognitive functions but with our nervous system and how our nervous system and brain have evolved.

1

This video visualizes our brain and the three parts: reptilian, limbic and neocortex.

What we want to allow for is that earlier and older parts of our nervous system (our reptilian and limbic system), whose function is to keep us as an individual alive and well, to provide the safety that allows for the latest edition of our nervous system.

---

1.   https://www.youtube.com/watch?v=FTnCMxEnnv8

This is our vagal nerve and prefrontal cortex, to do what it is designed for to engage socially - and to allow us as an individual as well as others to stay safe, thrive and be well.

We want the last edition of our brain, our prefrontal cortex, to be in charge and take centre stage. As Dr. Dan Siegel explains in his book "The Developing Mind"[2], there are nine functions of the prefrontal cortex, including some specific human qualities: Body Regulation, Attuned Communication, Emotional Balance, Responsive Flexibility, Fear Modulation, Self-knowing Awareness, Empathy, Morality and Intuition.

Our prefrontal cortex allows us to organise, make sense of, and engage with other parts of our inner world that need to be connected and acknowledged while feeling free and safe.

Another capacity we have is our ability to witness this internal process, a capacity for awareness which allows for reflection. This capacity has no fixed identity and is sometimes described by people who have experienced a near-death or spiritual experience. Buddhism refers to this part of us as the - "No-Self". On the other hand, IFS refers to this capacity as the "Self", which it regards as a person's core, which contains leadership qualities such as compassion, calmness, clarity, curiosity, confidence, courage, creativity, and connectedness. We will expand on this later in the book.

The Subtitle of this book is "Embodied Recovery from Trauma and Addiction".

What I mean by embodied recovery is that we shouldn't expect to erase that which makes us suffer, literally heal or get rid of our pain, trauma, or grief. The wounding has occurred like a scar, and our body has responded accordingly. We can aim to build the capacity to co-exist with it in a way that allows

2.   https://drdansiegel.com/book/the-developing-mind/

other qualities like presence, joy, and safety to be there. So, in accepting the wound, the scar, we can "re-cover" qualities such as goodness, joy, peace, relief, connection, presence, and simplicity to emerge (again).

This book contains a combination of reflections, vision, passion, poetry, and hope. The topics and references in this book affected me and have been invaluable for my development, which I, at times, will briefly expand upon.

I recommend exploring these topics and references further if called to do so, as I realise my limitations in doing justice to the depth behind some models.

In the Appendix, you will find in addition to a summary of three models I refer to in this book: Integral Theory, Polyvagal Theory (PVT) and Internal Family Systems (IFS), and a link to examples of developmental maps for organisations supporting transitioning towards a trauma-integrated service.

I hope this book will support addiction services but also invite personal reflection on the current addiction and recovery paradigm – What does addiction and recovery mean to you? -, the paradigms limitations and for this book to plead for and promote a new direction. A direction for addiction treatment to become more inclusive, to include the role of physiology in treatment and recovery, become more integrative, clarify the role and function of addiction, increase a sense of hope, become more effective and show opportunities for ongoing embodied recovery.

1. SHADOW DANCING

In 2017, when living in Vancouver with my partner, Therese, I volunteered at the Carnegie Community Centre in downtown Vancouver.

Downtown Vancouver is infamous for its homeless population and the high rate of people who live on the streets and use drugs.

Carnegie Community Centre[3] is an inspiring place offering free meals to homeless residents. They organise many classes, practical support and social-cultural gatherings. Membership is $1 annually, and the centre has many volunteers. I was one of them for several months, working in the kitchen and dining area.

Being interested in the history of Vancouver and its well-known addiction struggles in the downtown area, I watched a documentary shot in Vancouver showing two women who had just taken drugs. One of them just sat down, didn't move and experienced the anticipated drug-induced relaxation and dissociation; the other woman was physically chaotic, was moving around and shouted non-coherently. It seems her body moved independently, acting out a life of its own, making random and wild, seemingly involuntary movements as if the drugs were totally in control of her body.

---

3.   https://vancouver.ca/parks-recreation-culture/carnegie-community-centre.aspx

Learning about physiology and our nervous system (more about that later) allowed me to understand what I witnessed: trauma stories are carried in states of autonomic dysregulation, as I learned from Dr. Stephen Porges. Using substances might and can be considered an attempt to balance the system.

Depending on the physiological state someone is in, the effects will vary. So, the woman with the wild movements activated her sympathetic nervous system, i.e., fight or flight, and the sedated woman activated her dorsal vagus parasympathetic system, which allowed her to be numb and disconnected.

In both examples, using the metaphor of Shadow Dancing would not be accurate as we see the nervous system acting on its own (limbic and reptilian brain), separate from the part (prefrontal cortex) that would be able to dance with the shadow consciously. There was no integration, and there seemed to be no conscious awareness of what was happening. No association but dissociation.

From an IFS perspective, healing occurs when the Self can be in a supportive, loving, accepting relationship with the exile or protectors (managers/firefighters). That would be an example of a skill or capacity for healing, a process of self-regulation allowing for recovery.

Before this capacity or a process of self-healing can occur, someone must first have had an experience of co-regulation, either in the early years as a secure, trusting attachment environment and/or later between significant others or between a therapist and client.

Experiencing co-regulation is a biological imperative. When someone experiences healing, i.e. has not only a subjective experience of healing but also, at the same time, an objective, more witnessing experience, is aware of the process, then someone has grown this capacity and developed the skill to self-regulate and self-heal when needed.

This is the process that Shadow Dancing is pointing to. It is a process that focuses on allowing a welcoming, conscious relationship with the shadow, subjectively and as a witness compassionately "being with" the expressions and experience of the body and nervous system states and awareness of possibly old narratives that can surface and be reflected upon.

My felt limitations of the tools/support that I was able to offer to clients over the years and the lack of ambition and innovation by the "addiction industry" made me feel frustrated. This motivated me to find alternative and complementary ways to address the difficulties and obstacles clients told me about.

I realised that most skills taught by addiction services focused primarily on cognitive approaches such as CBT and motivational interviewing, which are well-researched and embedded in addiction services.

From an IFS perspective, emphasis on cognitive approaches would strengthen the part of the manager and bypass and sit on top of the firefighter part and exile. You can imagine the part that wants recognition and doesn't feel welcome (exile) and the firefighter part, which reacts to situations to prevent the exile part from being triggered, which means to feel its fears and feelings, won't appreciate that.

This is one of the main reasons that people in recovery can still be fearful and prone to relapse, as their exile part has not been sufficiently integrated. The exile remains sensitive to triggers. Current approaches play out our cognitive ability against the wisdom of our nervous system instead of allowing them to become connected and integrated.

Examples of strengthening the manager skills that you will find in most addiction services are linked with emphasising cognitive techniques with clients. For example:

❖ making a pro-/con- list of advantages and disadvantages of using substances

❖ looking at triggers and strategies to avoid/deal with them

❖ giving info and advice on how to go about dealing with anxiety, depression, sleep hygiene

❖ discussing ways to adhere to taking prescribed medication and plans or goals on how to reduce or stop these

❖ using schematic connections between emotions, thoughts, interpretations and behaviour

❖ making commitments to attending support groups and setting goals

Cognitive approaches generally promote a measurable, materialistic perspective and change is considered relatively linear, logical, and quantifiable as long as you follow the "rational" approach. They are deemed evidence-based, promote a sense of control and allow for a feeling of agency.

Cause and Effect

Cognitive models are typically based on the relationship between cause and effect.

Example: the narrative is that opiate dependence (cause) creates withdrawal symptoms (effect) due to a lack of opiates being present, or withdrawal symptoms (cause) require opiates (effect) to rebalance opiate levels.

This perspective is promoted in our culture and frames a complex challenge as substance misuse as a relatively straightforward cause–effect problem that needs to be fixed, i.e., we tell you what you are missing, and we will provide the fix, the solution.

You can also see this model played out in advertisements, the educational system, the financial world, etc. This problem exists; we know what to do and have this solution for you.

Pavlov's operant conditioning research of the dog conditioned to expect food (as evidenced by salivating) after hearing a bell has contributed to this (mechanistic) perspective.

Looking at the physiology of the dog, whose nervous system includes the reptilian and limbic brain functionality, this causality is more deterministic for the dog than for us as we also have a prefrontal cortex allowing us to be aware of this causality and in doing so, enables choice in how we can respond in a situation.

Using a "Cause-Effect" model is too simplistic to capture what is happening within humans, and this model inherently limits and underestimates our capacities.

Including our physiology, our feedback system, specifically our nervous system (including our prefrontal cortex), into the equation – makes for:

Cause – Physiology – Effect.

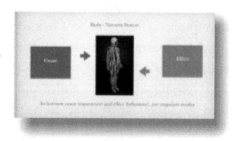

Another way to visualise the hierarchy of our information processing path is that the effect is determined by the cause, our nervous system state, feelings, behaviour and narrative.

Cause - State - Feelings - Behaviour - Narrative - Effect

Physiology

Physiology is the branch of biology that studies normal functions within living organisms and their parts. For our purpose, the part of physiology most related to the topic of this book, which is our shadow/trauma part, is our nervous system.

Dr. Stephen Porges, an American neuroscientist, points out in his Polyvagal Model[1] that in addition to the well-known fight and flight response in situations of danger, there is also the freeze response that shuts down the nervous system as a way to protect and survive a potentially life-threatening situation.

Trauma stories are carried in states of autonomic dysregulation, which is what we learned from Dr. Porges. The Appendix at the end of this book contains a summary of the Polyvagal Theory.

---

1.   https://polyvagal-institute.mn.co/

Dr Porges reminded us that the vagal pathway, the vagal nerve, is a highway, providing information in 2 directions from and to the body and the brain, with 80% of the lead going from the body to the brain (afferent or sensory neurons) and 20% of information going from the brain to the body (efferent or motor neurons).

In our society, performance is usually measured in productivity. We try to measure what success is for a human being, yet this is not a linear process. Our brains are compared to machines, but we are not machines. Our nervous systems are complex; with a machine, you put something in and get something out. We are a complex system, creative and have emergent properties.

People prefer to avoid conceptualising complexity and include, for example, feedback loops that we take into account. A linear system is the sum of the parts, whereas emergent systems have the potential to create and become more than the sum of the parts.

An environment that wants to allow and care for emergent systems needs to meet criteria like trust and safety to create conditions for those qualities to come forth.

Changing perception from considering addiction an illness to a coping strategy requires including and integrating what has been missing so far in addiction treatment: our body and nervous system.

The vital contribution of the poly-vagal theory is that it clarifies the critical role that our nervous system plays in our lives and, from that perspective, gives words and provides a narrative for behaviours that before were mysterious and unexplained, like fawning and freezing.

Questions clients regulary ask when they seek support for their addiction are:

- "What happened with me?"

- "How did I end up where I am now?"

- "Why is it that I can't control my behaviour?".

Considering these questions, the Polyvagal Model invites us to, in addition to other factors, include our understanding of our physiology, particularly our nervous system.

From an evolutionary perspective[2], the first vagal branch started in prehistoric animals around 500 million (!) years ago with the dorsal vagal nerve (connecting with the organs under the diaphragm), and its job was and is to care for our digestive system.

From there, around 400 million years ago, we evolved with our increasing sympathetic ability to respond more effectively, connect more to our environment, and use physiological movement to fight or flight when our survival demands it.

The ventral vagal nerve is the latest branch to emerge from our nervous system around 200 million years ago. This addition allowed us to experience an increased sense of safety, connectedness, and closeness. It allowed for social connections and exchanges.

---

2.   https://www.sciencedirect.com/science/article/pii/S0301051122001259

Neuroception

Separate branches of the vagal nerve are activated or deactivated depending on the information received. This information is neither verbal nor cognitive; it arrives and is processed before we become aware. Dr. Porges named this capacity neuroception. Neuroception describes how the autonomic nervous system takes in information without involving the thinking parts of the brain; this process runs in the background before cognitive awareness.

The word neuroception points to the combination of "neuro" (nervous system) and "ception" (awareness). Neuroception responds to cues of safety and danger.

Some examples of neuroception:

- ❖ inside the body (heart rate, breathing)
- ❖ outside in the environment (sounds, movement)
- ❖ between people (relational quality)

Physiology trumps intention as that process happens before we tap into our executive functions and use our cognition (prefrontal cortex) / intentionality.

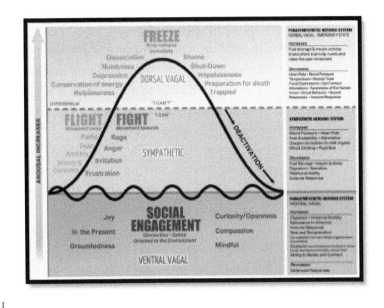

1

When our nervous system detects danger (through neuroception), the sympathetic nervous system (fight or flight) gets activated, and our cognitive function (linked with our vagal nerve) shuts down. Our body is triggered to act; our blood pressure increases, our muscles are ready to mobilise, our digestive system slows down, our heart rate increases and our pupils dilate.

When the threat is not eliminated, and our fight/flight response does not have the desired effect, our nervous system activates our dorsal vagal nerve and shuts our system down. This can manifest as

Fainting, dissociation, numbness, feeling sleepy. Our cognitive functions at that point are put on standby and are not online, activated, or functional.

1.   https://corkpsychotherapyandtraumacentre.ie/trauma/polyvagal-theory

This knowledge about the function of our nervous system and how it works, when it works and how there are stages in nervous system activation informs us how we influence and can support someone who experiences anxiety or depression.

Deb Dana[2] described three predictable hierarchical ways of nervous system response as follows:

❖ The parasympathetic nervous system ventral vagus: a system of safety and connection aiming for health, growth and restoration.

❖ The sympathetic nervous system: a system of mobilisation aiming for protection through action.

❖ The parasympathetic nervous system dorsal vagus: a system of immobilisation: protection through disappearing.

We communicate with our nervous systems when we meet someone; we should be aware of this, especially as health professionals. Our nervous system influences our ability to create a safe environment, make someone feel safe, be curious, and exchange and retain information.

That is why listening to and witnessing other people's experiences is important instead of evaluating and judging them (which can activate a sense of unsafety and anxiety).

Being an open, curious, caring witness to someone else's experience enhances connection.

2.   https://youtu.be/JXGy7M4kvaY?si=zclrx00RzZzhTkmi

We become aware of the importance of our physiological state and how our facial expressions and tone of voice (prosody) are integral to our nervous system regulation. We affect someone else by how we feel.

Research shows that the quality of the therapeutic relationship is directly related to the outcome of treatment, and this is particularly important for clients who engage in addictive processes (Miller & Rollick, 2013).

I remember that my teacher, Prof. Christine Caldwell, said, "Our body is our first intervention" in one of her workshops, which was an eye-opener for me and struck me as so true when I heard it.

As therapists, making someone feel safe in our presence is a core skill so they can relax and become curious about what comes up from within without needing to be overly concerned about safety in their environment or acceptance by the therapist.

It can be that neuroception gives cues of danger when no actual threat is present or that the good intentions of the therapist trigger a cue of danger for the client. You can check with the client and ask a question that does not take the client to their brain (what do you think or how do you feel?), but you can ask, "How does this land for you in your system?" or "Where did your nervous system take you?" or "What is happening in your nervous system right now?".

You want to check in with the client about their state. Do they see me (does the client's neuroception sense me) as a restorative resource or a threat?

Being safer does not necessarily make us feel safer. Many of our social systems are focused on the features of danger, yet we have a profound sensitivity to safety features, and exposure to these can foster resilience.

A closer inspection of shadow also lets us discover that there is no isolated individual shadow but that there are multitudes of shadow expressions and a system of collective shadow that we keep alive in our culture and create together.

This is where an integral perspective (further discussed in the next chapter) can help us consider multiple perspectives so our understanding and response become more inclusive and compassionate.

An element of shadow is also stuckness in one perspective, not considering other viewpoints like an observer bias.

Observer bias is the tendency of observers not to see what is there but instead to see what they expect or want to see. In integral theory this is called "quadrant absolutism" (see also Chapter 2) and it is similar to our coping mechanism of "compartimentalisation".

One of my shadows as a teenager was linked to insecurity and needing an activity to develop my confidence. In my situation, losing myself in the game of chess, as taught to me by my father, provided some relief.

Playing chess from the age of around fourteen became an escape from insecurity and feeling a dis-ease with myself and the world around me. It was also a way for me to structure my

time, and it gave me a much-needed increase in s
and a sense of self-worth as an adolescent v
winning some games.

Playing chess made me feel safe as I could live temporarily in a world within sixty-four squares.

I realised, only recently, that playing chess also made me play small, keeping my focus and interest confined within 64 squares. Chess can be considered a metaphor for a relatively simple and secure life. Nowadays, you can play chess everywhere on mobile phones in the palm of your hand.

In the process of writing this book, I noticed that there is still a relationship between when I feel stressed and playing chess. Learning about the Polyvagal Model, learning that chess is a stress-regulating tool for me, and connecting more in areas where I feel challenged have made me more resilient in finding strategies to deal with stress. I now recognise culturally accepted ways, like playing chess, as a possible nervous system regulator.

From psychology, we know that a well-recognised dilemma in early childhood presents itself when a child is faced with a choice between authenticity and attachment. Considering our early developmental skills and the reality that we depend on the people who care for us, as a child, we will almost always choose attachment over authenticity when pressed as our lives depend on it.

From a psychological perspective, it is not so much that the process of needing to choose is complex as it is that, in most cases, adults in our lives do not support us or educate us about that choice, including all the dimensions that are in play at that moment. Most of the time, we are educated on how to fit in rather than explore curiously and with validation of all the different responses, feelings and perspectives we experience.

If an adult would sit with us, create a safe and supporting space and help us - a child - in a challenging and maybe overwhelming situation to process and support the emotions that arise and would accurately be aware of what we were capable of regarding handling and integrating our experiences, that would allow for a most precious learning process.

In a not sufficiently resourced environment, when a child is forced to make meaning in a (too) difficult situation, there will be a sense of inadequacy due to a lack of support, which is appropriate for a child who has no skills yet to deal with such a situation. The child can internalise this situation and create a self-belief of "I am not good enough" instead of a realisation that "I am not yet capable of dealing with this situation, and that this is not my fault as I am still a young child".

This overwhelm or cognitive dissonance that a child can experience would be an example where a child could create a split between, or dissociate, in the child's sense of Self. When a client tells me about an experience like that, I explain this process and tell them that I call this an example of "environmental failure" where the client wasn't sufficiently supported.

So when an internal split happens in a child to deal with their experience, one part will be focused on staying on good terms with the people the child is dependent upon. Another part feels that it is struggling and inadequate as it cannot express and be acknowledged for its impulses and needs lovingly and thoroughly. That part is not accepted.

From an early age, I was lucky to have intuited a sense and understanding that we as individuals are an undivided "one", which has merit from a spiritual perspective. From that position, we always have been and always will be undivided, whole and ever-present.

Yet our worldly, embodied experience, growth, education, development and sensory interactions are about division, duality, diversity, complexity and change. Simply put, it is a world of multitudes.

This multitude and wide range of experiences involve experiencing different parts and multiple drivers, feeling a pull between opposites, and sometimes feeling torn and fragmented.

To add to the complexity, some parts that came into being when we were very young may not be accessible via our cognition or memory that could inform us what has happened in our earlier years. Some parts might have been experienced via our somatic senses ... a strong sense of dis-ease, strong reactions to triggers like a smell, a particular facial expression or an environment resembling a similar context to where (earlier) trauma happened.

Being open and receptive to signals and experiences from our body that point us towards understanding contraction, stress, feelings of disease, numbness, and feelings of anxiety/depression can bring us into contact with parts that need inquiry, compassionate care, and understanding.

Internal Family Systems[3] (IFS) by Richard Schwartz and the "Legacy of Trauma"[4] approach by Janina Fisher, who specialised in ways to understand and relate to the legacy of

3.   https://ifs-institute.com/

trauma and experience of dissociation, show convincing benefits and effectiveness of working with this model of integration considering the Self as the total sum of our parts (categorisations) and more (emergent properties).

The sense of Self is an experience I had to consciously develop and recognise, as my environment did not teach me this aspect in my education nor invite me to pay attention to my direct multi-perspectival experience. I was, and collectively, we can (and should) be explicitly taught about the existence and importance of our sense of Self.

When I was working in London with a client I will name Anna (fictitious name), she taught me the limitations of the cognitive treatment approaches that I used, was trained in, and how much I dismissed information from our nervous system as an indicator and source of discernment about what is important in a situation, what is needed, how to communicate, pay attention to our physiology and how this information informs us about what is going on. I will come back to Anna and her journey in the next chapter.

As I was looking for ways to include other streams of information other than cognition, Prof. Christine Caldwell's book "Getting Our Bodies Back" validated my experience and what I was missing and, with the support of her training, allowed me to trust again in my own (bodily) experience.

It introduced me to a vocabulary, how to pay attention, speak about my felt sense and navigate my way using a process developed by Christine Caldwell called "The Moving Cycle".[5]

---

4. https://youtu.be/n7RsL6elueA?si=d9V0sIfUtij1heMV

5. https://www.themovingcycle.com/

The Moving Cycle is a 4-step process that invites us first to become aware of our experience, listen, and tune into our body in the moment.

From this awareness, we invite associations that give us information about the origin, trigger, or relationship attached to that felt sense. By allowing the body to follow the impulses that arise by being present with the felt sense of the body and the associations, a new phase in the model starts, which is called appreciation. This phase lets us stay with and appreciate the newly emerged situation and notice its qualities and sensations. From this place, slowly, one can become more curious about how this can be integrated and find a place in one's life, relationships, skills, goals, etc. This phase is called the action phase.

Resistance in relating to and turning our focus towards our body has been a significant theme in my life. This process involves shifting our perspective from a 3rd person perspective (observing or considering an object from a distance) to a 1st person perspective, focusing on our direct experience and knowing that to be accurate, meaningful, imperfect and partial but valuable.

These experiences convey information about reality, ourselves and the world.

Information that withheld me from focusing on my experience and taking this seriously is the inherent presence of partiality, loss and death, which carries an intrinsic weight and a sobering quality that I needed to familiarise myself with gradually over time. I still struggle with that sometimes.

My experience was that considering things and events as an observer (3rd person) allows for distance and "objectivity", which has a cognitive, abstract, timeless element. Whereas allowing a 1st person sensory perspective, for me, this was associated with a greater sense of finite time as a mortal being, experiencing and simultaneously feeling anxiety as I realised I would be losing this capacity to handle this rich palette of mysterious colours, smells, rhythms, tactile sensations, interoception, neuroception, presence .... due to inevitable decline, loss, illness, diminishing capacities over time and the unavoidable experience of physical death and decay..... Tough stuff, indeed.

The culture I grew up in through education, TV, radio, books, etc., missed the importance of listening to our body and valuing our direct experience.

I now realise I grew up in a culture of somatophobia, which is the suspicion that our culture took on board and passed on to all its members almost unnoticeable, that has to do with doubting the information our body gives us.

This seems to be a natural side-effect of our educational system's emphasis on predominantly being focused on and promoting our cognitive intellect, memory, and external media information.

The proclamation and well-known exclamation of Descartes, "I think, therefore I am", inherently points to the special status we give to our intellect and cognition. A possible motivation, I assume, was to emphasise our difference from other mammals, promoting a sense of "specialness". This position did not encourage nor celebrate our similarities and that we are primarily connected in our "mammalian" make-up

21

with the sentient beings around us, nor with the biosphere in general - even though our body is part and parcel and unmistakably interconnected with nature.

Interoception

Interoception is our ability to feel our body and its relationship with its environment from the inside out. A well-known way to do this is the body scan, where one turns attention to different areas of the body, usually starting by checking in with our feet and going all the way up gradually to the crown of the head.

Other examples of interoception are the process of focusing (focusing is an experiential, embodied and evidence-based practice of self-reflection), mindfulness and mediation.

We also have a capacity for dual focus, which I will return to in Chapter 4. Dual focus is our ability to be present to 2 or more perspectives simultaneously. This is our ability to witness what is happening and, in doing so, have an awareness of the space in which different realities play out. As an example, in my training as a somatic practitioner, I became aware of how my mind took the position of an observer, taking a back seat (like sitting in the stalls in a theatre), whilst my body became my primary point of focus (i.e. taking centre stage in the theatre).

In dual focus, blending life energy with a part of yourself, i.e., identifying yourself with a part of you, becomes less intense and more transparent. This allows you to become more curious from a place of "not knowing, " enabling you to take in and integrate multiple information sources.

The state I was in (witnessing capacity) was aware of the theatre context, what happened on stage (i.e. body), and the audience (i.e. mind).

This would be the same state that one can experience in a healing context; namely, one could get back in touch with a wounded child part (exile) in oneself and, whilst grounded in a safe felt sense, be able to stay with and connect with the injured part which allows for healing and soothing of that part that endured the wound in the past. This is an example of an intra-relational self-healing activity which can be empowering and inspiring.

Our ordinary consciousness, in general, is focused on completing 1 task at a time and learning in a linear way, which we are conditioned to do. Concentrate on information outside ourselves and work with well-defined tasks, processes and realities.

Tuning inwards towards our sense of self can initially feel unfamiliar and a difficult place to start for someone who is not used to that or someone with a history of trauma, as reminders of trauma can be triggered. Tuning into ourselves, we use our capacity for interoception that allows us to be aware of how our body feels from the inside out, our thoughts, and our emotions. This is in contrast to exteroception, which points towards focusing on the world outside us, the environment, when we use our five senses of vision, hearing, smell, touch and taste.

Using interoception can make us feel more vulnerable, especially if we have had an experience where we experienced a loss of control over what happened. As a result, we can experience feeling unsafe, and our survival mechanism can kick in to feel safe again by activating our nervous system survival strategies, i.e. fighting, fleeing or freezing.

Two main parts in our brain affected by trauma are our hippocampus, which is involved in experiencing a timeline like the beginning, middle and end of an event and the amygdala, whose job it is to detect cues for danger so it can keep us safe by activating our survival responses if necessary.

Janina Fisher points out that the goal of treatment is not so much to heal or erase previous difficult emotions or experiences but to focus on improving the quality of life for the client.

The process of healing will look different for every person as the consequences in the here and now of the trauma will be unique for every person.

It is unnecessary to go back and relive the traumatic experiences in the past if you feel that does not help you. But if you can and want to address the trauma, much can be learned from and integrated through that journey.

It is taking your body and experience seriously and allowing it to guide you as you consider possible different paths emerging in that process.

Safe Enough

A sense of safety is critical in working with the shadow of your traumatic past if you choose to do that.

Here are some strategies to regulate your nervous system with your breath:

You can relax your nervous system by taking a full breath and, in addition to that breath, taking another little breath on top of your inhale. Then, allow for a long exhale. And notice how that makes you feel.

When we inhale, our heart rate increases slightly; when we exhale, our heart rate drops. We can consciously use this knowledge of our breath when our nervous system is wired (i.e. in a fight- or flight state) or in a hypo-aroused state (i.e. passive, freeze state).

When we want to relax, we can extend our exhale to lower our heart rate; for example, inhale for four counts and exhale for six or eight counts. This signals to our nervous system that there is safety.

This also works the other way around. When we want to become more energetic and active, we can allow our inhalation to be more extended than our exhalation, for example, taking a six- or eight-count inhalation to a four-count exhalation.

These are examples of a bottom-up approach to regulating our nervous systems using the body.

Another way to feel grounded, safe, and connected with our environment is by using our vocal cords and throat area. We can enjoy humming to experience more safety. The vibrations in your mouth and throat and hearing the sounds give off safety cues and are non-threatening. Humming has a long history, from when we were babies, and culturally, it has been used in soothing rituals. See if you can discover how your body responds to the vibrations that accompany the sound.

Feelings of being stuck, which many people experience in their addiction, have long been thought of as a cognitive defect or a lack of skills where a client does not realise the many options available. The narrative is that if only they could see these options, they could overcome obstacles, and new possibilities would open up.

In a treatment setting, this perspective focuses primarily on cognitive models, workbooks, exercises, explorations and advice that the key worker might provide to the client to fill that supposed lack of knowledge or skills.

Using our understanding of physiology and nervous system regulation, a feeling of being stuck, understood from a nervous system perspective, can be seen as an expression of the freeze response, which communicates from a physiological standpoint that there is a threat, a lack of safety and simultaneously the activation of the sympathetic nervous system that wants to fight or flight. The term "being addicted" is a good example of this state. To use a metaphor, it is trying to drive a car and step on the gas and brake pedals simultaneously. This activates both the sympathetic and parasympathetic nervous system.

From that perspective, the first step that needs to be considered is to acknowledge and accept what is happening in the moment - feeling stuck and unsafe - and to use the energy of the sympathetic nervous system for curiosity about the felt sense of stuckness and to consider this feeling as an opportunity to learn, develop and increase our window of tolerance.

To tap into the self-healing capacity of our bodies, first and foremost, an experience of safety is needed. This allows the nervous system to relax and the prefrontal cortex to get online, allowing for an increasing sense of connection and safety.

The presence of a support worker can provide clarity if needed and support the client's process, which creates an additional layer of connection, safety and healing. One of our most underestimated needs as human beings is to be seen and understood for nothing more and nothing less than what we are: an ongoing process of infinite learning, deepening development, widening discoveries and evolutionary becoming.

Allowing the client to connect with what is happening in his experience without judgment in the here and now is an act of mindfulness. Again, being present is a great regulator of our nervous system, as the ventral vagal nerve is allowed and invited to be online.

The experience of being and feeling stuck, which we could reduce to a view or category which is then boxed in, considered as an object that is "known" and either liked or not liked, can, through mindfulness, be transformed into an experience of a dialectic process, a process that is alive and uses our ability to experience and at the same time be aware of our experience.

Being aware of the experience in the moment allows for the energy or lack of energy we experience to be acknowledged and compassionately welcomed and cared for as a part of ourselves that shows itself and, therefore, needs and wants to be accepted, respected, seen, held and appreciated.

Psychology tells us that the opponent process theory explains the value of this process as this process points out that when an emotion has reached its peak - either a low or a high - it will give birth to the emergence of its opposite feeling and increases the capacity to connect and integrate that emotion.

Some questions to consider/reflect upon if you like:

❖ What is your experience at this moment?

❖ What is your ability to ground and feel safe?

❖ Can you be with your experience wholeheartedly?

❖ Are you aware of your window of tolerance?

What follows is a text from Rob de Koning about trauma.

"Your fear is not imaginary.

Your fear of rejection not belonging is real ......

This is the brutal truth your little one experienced exactly this......... So, there is no need to change or to fix this, No need to run away or to solve it (her)... As a problem.
Cause this little precious one isn't a problem to be solved or medicated. This little one needs to be seen, heard, and acknowledged.....
She doesn't need a how to do list, or teachings how to change........ Cause there is nothing wrong with her. So instead of, to get rid of her or to get over her..... Just stop.
Imagine her in the corner of your room as a real person, a real being.
A frightened and scared little girl......... How should you react .....

Should you say "please go away" or "you might come back when you are "normal".
Or should you open your heart ....I am really sorry it's
the first time I see you...
Or You might be filled with joy just to meet this little one......
It might be the first time this little one has the courage to
show herself.
Instead of what you think, this might be an invitation.
You, remembering a lost part of yourself.......

You might not know the way she communicate as of yet, the language she uses........but remember it's still a child and this is her way of getting your attention.......

No words are necessary; just sit still and be present wit her ....
She don't want to be healed, she just want to be held .... ◈☺

And remember your little girl is not crazy she just experienced some crazy stuff."

Rob de Koning

2. ADDICTION TREATMENT

"Addiction", according to the Merriam-Webster dictionary, as a verb is first known to be used in 1612.

Addiction at that time meant "to give over, surrender, apply or devote (oneself) habitually", borrowed from the Latin word "Addictus".

Considering the word "addiction" from a nervous system perspective, its etymology is interesting as the root of the word addiction can be interpreted as "going towards ("ad") speaking or saying ("dice").

The effect of addiction on our physiology can be all-consuming and so overwhelming that integration between our right-brain hemisphere (emotional and sensation sensitive) and our left-brain hemisphere (structuring, naming, referencing) becomes compromised.

From that perspective, addiction can be considered a challenge of how to increase our understanding and integration of the right- and left-brain hemispheres.

Integral Perspectives

My map of reality is greatly influenced by philosopher and writer Ken Wilber[1] who emphasises the importance and consideration of at least four dimensions of any given challenge to do justice to the complexity of most problems or situations.

The integral map encompasses several key elements. The essentials of this map are a matrix referred to as "AQAL", which stands for all Quadrants, all Levels, all Lines, all States and all Types.

Here are two visual versions of his Quadrants map emphasising different qualities:

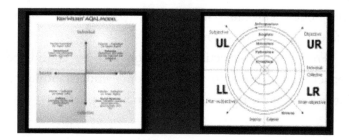

The diagonal arrows in the right picture represent the development over time of capacities in all four quadrants

through evolution, where the centre of the picture represents the start of evolution (Big Bang).

The Appendix provides a link to examples of organisational development models using these maps as they are sufficiently comprehensive for complex and multi-level tasks.

Here is a short overview of the different quadrants:

Upper left quadrant / Individual internal (subjective):

What is the experience of the person with the addiction? How does it feel, what is the meaning, and what is the narrative and self-identity that is affected by addiction for the individual?

Lower left quadrant / Collective internal (inter-subjective):

What is the perception of the culture towards addiction? How does this come to expression in language, the media, and the people's perspective in family, county, and country circles?

Curiosity about what addiction is and how it is that in the press, almost without exception, exaggerated stories surfaced about out-of-control situations with often shocking outcomes brought me to the choice to work in an addiction detox/rehab placement during my nursing education.

That way, I could discover what is true about all those dramatic stories. So, to put it in the context of the quadrants, a lower left motivation drove me.

<u>Upper right quadrant / Individual external (objective):</u>

How does addiction affect the body? How does taking drugs, alcohol, and gambling affect the brain?

What is the process of neurotransmitters? How are hormones and nervous system reactions affected?

<u>Lower right quadrant / Collective external (inter-objective):</u>

What are the systems and infrastructure dealing with addiction? How are probation services involved, and what are the courses and treatment options available?

Perspectives on addiction have changed dramatically over the years, where it was initially considered a moral flaw, then a sin, then a choice, then an illness and a chronic relapsing disease.

All these perspectives have some truths yet do not cover the complex internal dynamics beneath the service of behaviour that we call addiction. And this is reflected in the poor outcomes of our current treatment approaches.

Development, Growth

Development (or growth or evolution) occurs in all four quadrants. When science studies the right-hand quadrants, it finds the evolution of galaxies, stars, planets, and species. When psychology studies the upper left quadrant, it finds developmental stages we all pass through. And when social scientists study the two lower quadrants, they find the evolution of cultures and societies.

Psychologists who study human development find that in childhood and youth, we move quickly through stages of development up to young adulthood. But when we reach our mid-twenties, growth tends to stop, often for decades.

My experience is that development in addiction services - and more generally in mental health - has been overly focused on the medical model, the right-hand side of the map. Effectiveness has been compromised by neglecting attention and development on the left-hand side of the map - the subjective and inter-subjective dimensions. The map shows that development must co-occur in all dimensions simultaneously to be balanced and effective.

The UK government requested an independent review of the current addiction treatment structure in 2021 by Dame Carol Black. Here is a quote from Dame Carol Black's report[1] about addiction services in the UK:

"It must be recognised that addiction is a chronic health condition, and like diabetes, hypertension or rheumatoid arthritis, it will require long-term follow-up. Discharge after

---

1.   https://www.bmj.com/content/374/bmj.n1828

short-term treatment is currently used as a measure of success but should be stopped, as it ignores the condition's fundamental relapsing and remitting nature.

Trauma (physical, sexual or psychological) and mental ill-health are drivers and accompaniment of much addiction.

They are co-morbidities rather than particular problems for a 'dual diagnosis'. Commissioners of substance misuse services and NHS mental health services must ensure that individuals do not fall between the cracks. (...) For many people, mental health problems and trauma lie at the heart of their drug and alcohol dependence. However, they are too often excluded from mental health services until they resolve their drug problem, and they are excluded from drug services until their mental health problems have been addressed. (...). The workforce in both services should be trained to better respond to co-existing drug and mental health problems."

For an addiction treatment service to consider including trauma-informed care or, even better, trauma-integrated care, Janina Fisher states three core assumptions of a trauma model in relation to addiction:

> 1. For traumatised clients, any self-destructive behaviour begins as a post-traumatic survival strategy aimed at regulating autonomic arousal.

> 2. The problem results because these behaviours require continual "dosage" (tolerance) increases to maintain effectiveness; eventually, they become more chronic, severe, and less effective.

3. Treatment must address the relationship between the trauma and the addictive behaviour: the role of the addiction in "medicating" traumatic activation and the reality that <u>recovering from either requires recovering from both.</u>

Awareness about trauma is an essential first step.

So how do we make this concrete and embedded in organisations?

The Crisis & Trauma Resource Institute (CTRI)[2] suggests the following steps:

❖ allow a shift in attitudes
❖ foster safety
❖ provide choice
❖ focus on strength

The first step, changing attitudes, might be the most challenging step for addiction services.

There has been a history of regarding addiction as a chronic relapsing illness in the last 100 years, promoted culturally by the popularity of the 12-step movement founded in the 1930's.

Due to the medicalisation in the addiction field and its focus on pathology - addiction is predominantly viewed as similar to a physical illness; for example, for clients who have a heroin dependency, medication (legal opiates) is used to replace heroin (illegal opiates).

This can be viewed as a harm-minimisation strategy, which has its merits as it buys time for the client to stabilise and increase so-called "recovery capital"[3]. Recovery capital, a term

2.　　https://ctrinstitute.com/

introduced and researched by David Best, is generally considered the breadth and depth of internal and external resources that can be drawn upon to initiate and sustain recovery reference.

The current treatment model widely accepted in the UK and internationally, with its roots firmly set in USA soil and branching out worldwide, is called MAT (Medication Assisted Treatment).

The goal of MAT is to motivate the client to engage with the addiction service and to accept, in the case of opiate addiction, opiate replacement medication, which is prescribed daily. The plan is for the client to become less dependent on illegal drugs as now a free legal alternative is available. The dose will then be slowly and safely increased and maintained to a level that the client feels is sufficient and where the need for taking other illicit drugs is not required for their physical dependency.

Dependency on other drugs like cannabis, cocaine, hallucinogens or process addictions (i.e. gambling, sex) is supported by a variety of primarily cognitive therapies where behaviour change is set as the goal and seen as the requirement for recovery.

How this plays out from my first-hand experience on the work floor and how this affects the demanding working conditions for professionals and volunteers in addiction services:

3.   https://calrecovery.org/category/recovery-capital/

❖ An increasing number of clients are allocated to a key worker (someone who is the point of contact for a client and who has contact with a client frequently, on average, around fortnightly). It is not uncommon for a key worker to have a caseload of sixty clients or more.

❖ Due to service requirements of verifiable written evidence of steps that an addiction service (i.e. key worker) has taken regarding risk management, required actions undertaken by the service are added to the client's file so there is evidence the client was informed about risks of behaviour, medication, environment, etc.

❖ Few clients successfully exit treatment. My estimation is ~ 10% which David Best[4] confirms is what addiction workers in this field agree with. Some clients are in treatment services for over 20 years, and there is an increasing need for places as demand grows.

❖ More clients enter treatment when the social-economic situation deteriorates, and living conditions become more challenging. For example, a significant increase in alcohol dependency was noted due to COVID lockdowns, which increased stress and social isolation.

---

4. https://youtu.be/33q9E9EBtww?si=gwD75X5NKaEJACwi

❖ Addiction treatment has been set up as a risk-averse measurable business with a streamlined input, throughput, and output focussing on data and quantifiable parameters, i.e. changes in consumption, behaviour, prescribed medication dose, number of missed appointments, etc.

The low positive, consistent outcomes of successfully treating addiction and dependency have made services look for other ways to report success.

For example, they have made significant investments in staff allocation and funds aiming for secondary wins focussed on harm minimisation, which are essential. However, shouldn't they address their core business of addiction treatment primarily? Some examples of these activities are hepatitis screening and treatment, vaccination clinics, ECG monitoring, liver scans, blood tests, etc. All these measurable "objective" activities can be evidenced and compared.

This emphasis on harm minimisation takes away from the core business of addiction treatment: supporting clients to reduce their dependency or leave their addiction behind. For me, at this moment in time, it shows that addiction services do not have a sufficient belief or conviction that they can successfully support someone to heal their addiction. What I mean by that is to develop and offer support to someone to transform and gain different skill sets and interior perspectives, including speaking about relationships with shadows, triggers, and most likely experienced trauma, which could be addressed by a specialised service if required.

Achieved recovery (successful exit from addiction treatment) is accomplished by a minority of clients, not considering the number of people re-entering treatment after a relapse.

These depressing numbers and conclusions were a big motivation for me to grow my skillset with trauma-informed and somatic-based perspectives and skills.

Key workers are at high risk for burnout due to the high number of clients they connect with, the administrative demands that require them to report up-to-date risk management in detail in the client's file, relatively few numbers of long-term progress from clients and the risk for vicarious trauma from clients who share their traumatic history and struggles associated with their untreated trauma.

A shift in attitude requires a shift from believing addiction to be a pathology to understanding the function of addiction to be a strategy that allows clients to cope the best they can.

This also implies a shift in power dynamics where addiction service workers and managers shift from a position where they think they know what is best for the client (behaviour-focused) to listening and following a client's lead into exploring the next best step and taking into account the journey and what happened to the client.

Nervous System Regulation

My first-hand experiences of working in addiction services taught me to know the pressures the system can put on staff and volunteers.

Some examples: a doctor who allowed five-minute appointments with clients ... key workers who book clients in throughout the whole day with little to no breaks ... colleagues skipping lunch or eating their lunch while working ... some colleagues I know have been coming in 45 minutes early in the morning so they can organise and prepare for the day / do some backlog admin work ... others are working overtime, sometimes not only at the office but also at home or in weekends ... I relate to some of them too.

How the current system is organised and managed affects staff, managers and, most importantly, clients. This culture has remained the same whilst funding for services has been cut, staff numbers reduced, and more clients than ever entered treatment, so the time available by addiction workers had to be shared in even more chunks for more and more clients.

There is no way around it ... if the client wants to heal their addiction, we need to be willing to create a safe and resourceful environment for clients - with the support of trained trauma-informed staff - to lean in safely and ready to go to the other side of stories ... through the landscape of emotions and feelings whilst supported by a (mental) health professional.

Most information on the internet or applications, remote contact, written communication, and training to increase knowledge all serve our cognitive minds ...

In equal measure, we want to focus on developing our emotional and spiritual intelligence. For those capacities to be seen, heard, valued, listened to, understood and developed more.

Here are some practical examples of including awareness of physiology in treatment.

Notice the following when someone experiences a freeze response:

❖ not allowing for eye contact
❖ matter-of-fact voice
❖ no or little movement

Some symptoms can be minimal (micro-movements) and complex to detect yet detectable. This is what emotional support dogs can do: they spot nervous system responses early and provide a supportive and appropriate response.

Possible actions:

Create a safe and welcoming environment (low intensity), encourage movement: singing, breathing, walking. Encourage them to engage in the present, use the senses, feel contact with the floor, look around the room or notice how you are sitting.

Background:

In a freeze state, the prefrontal cortex is offline; nothing new comes in until the freeze state relaxes. What is needed is right-brain-to-right-brain communication (body / nervous system communication and exchange). Avoid cognitive questions.

Possible strategy:

Shake your hand, nod your head. You can ask: are you feeling much fear? Can you move your eyes to see as far to the right as possible?

Go slowly....; use proximity and voice information, asking questions like: Can you look around the room? Can you describe something that you like? Identify and name some non-threatening things in the room.

If breathing is fast, you can reflect with the following: it looks like your breathing is so short. Could you breathe with me (focus on extending out-breath)?

Or you might say: "I want you to feel that I am here with you...." and let's see if we can make subtle movements together...

When someone asks, "What triggered the freeze response?" You can inform them that it was a nervous system experience and that the nervous system was looking out for the person to keep him safe.

When a client is more resilient, you can ask to observe the process of getting into a freeze state and coming out of it. What was your nervous system response coming out of the freeze?

You can use memory to go to the trigger experience ... go just before freeze when there is still movement, discover what it is that your body wants to do, allow for the body to execute the action and activities safely and savour the aftermath - emotions, pleasure, experience, feeling of empowerment.

Our history is revealed in the present moment ... and you can use the physiological information you observe as a reference point.

So, when we notice tension, then that needs attention. When we feel numb, then that needs attention, etc.

You can ask, "How about we stay with the tension in your shoulders?" and become curious to get more information from the tension.

When this happens in a home situation, people might like to feel the comfort of pressure (weighted blankets), or someone can offer pressure (holding or pressing safely hands) to support someone to get and feel grounded.

What you don't want to do:

❖ making eye contact too soon
❖ touching (ask for permission first)
❖ being too quick to ask for movement/permission
❖ give the impression this is a negative phenomenon

Other ways to make the client more familiar with the role of the nervous system are:

Create an individual profile map where the client maps out their experience in

❖ an activated/mobilised state (sympathetic nervous system) and the story that comes with it about themself and the world.

❖ and their narrative about themself and the world when they are in a ventral state (connected, calm, safe)

❖ and their narrative about themself and the world when in a dorsal state (immobilised, numb).

A Case Study

I had an experience in London whilst working in the National Health Service (NHS) with a client who was dependent on alcohol. I will call her Anna.

I was able to work with Anna for two years, and what I learned from her was that all the cognitive approaches that I was taught to offer did not land as she was very much identified with her body and focused on the effects of the alcohol on the body and her mind.

This escalated to the point where she couldn't walk to the shop anymore and buy alcohol. She started drinking cleaning fluid for alcohol content, ending up in A&E. I am glad to report that the alcohol detox she received in the hospital, with a short break in a nursing home for respite care, motivated her to choose a stay in a sober house, a residential rehab that she completed successfully.

At the time of her recovery, the clinical addictions group (CAG) was asked to give an example of their work. Anna and I were invited to share our experiences with the NHS board members of Kings College Hospital in London, which we did.

Here is the integral account from Anna and myself:

Presentation Boardroom 2015

"Paul: This is the story of Anna's journey, which has been unlike any other client I have worked with, which you will hear throughout the story. This is less about 'you said... we did' and more about 'you couldn't....we didn't know how to'.

Anna: I've been a client with Paul's team for about two years, being a frequent attender at A&E due to alcohol abuse. It's been a bleak and dangerous journey, in and out of A&E, several admissions into hospital, intensive care, hypothermia, lost days through blackouts and broken bones. I feel it's a miracle I've survived.

Paul's team offered various methods of support and help – but none worked for me. What the system offered wasn't working for me, and I wasn't working with what the system could offer.

I have been told that there are two sides to me: One is that when I'm sober, I can participate, I have my voice heard, and I can make decisions. The second is when I'm drunk – Paul and others have told me how different I can be then – I have blackouts and no memory of what I have said to people and little memory of what has been agreed.

Consequently, everything that was put in place has failed. I had agreed to things when temporarily sober, which I didn't agree with, or I would participate differently when intoxicated. You must remember that at times, I have been too weak to walk due to alcohol abuse I have gone through; when I was too weak to walk – I didn't know how to seek the right help. At those times, I craved alcohol, not psychiatric support.

My support network and friends couldn't support me at those times, and at one time, I turned to drinking cleaning fluids simply because of the alcohol content. You can't imagine what that was doing to me. My situation seemed pretty hopeless.

Paul: The project offered assertive outreach support with the support of volunteers to provide personalised care and reduce the number of presentations at A&E.

I worked with Anna's supportive network consisting of long-term friends and, with Anna's agreement, informed each other of the support needed and provided. 2 project volunteers were introduced to Anna, who could have regular contact to help out with practical and social activities.

I did over 80 home visits and accompanied Anna to and from the hospital, GP, nursing home (for respite care), detox, and rehab. In April 2015, the difficult decision was made to reduce the support offered by the project – as the support provided wasn't working – and Anna was offered weekly appointments at the project's location (Marina House). The interventions for Anna at some stage throughout the process did not work for her. We have often had many complex and challenging clients, but at some stage, one of the interventions would yield a more positive outcome.

For Anna, whatever we had to offer didn't work. Of course, the team continued to endeavour to see this through, but all avenues were beginning to close. Anna wasn't able to say 'you said' but was still screaming out for help – 'we did' but sadly unsuccessful. Then something changed.

My take on this is that Anna eventually saw her situation differently. My experience informed me that recovery is always informed and highly dependent on the individual's sense of self. Sometimes, that awareness doesn't include recovery yet, sometimes it never will (for multiple reasons), and sometimes it might happen quickly.

Psychiatric treatment and psychological intervention require both parties to work together, as a kind of symbiosis – when that happens, the chances of recovery increase.

There is a real need and importance for clinicians to listen and learn from the client's experience and stick with it. This is where Anna is now: a more inclusive 'working together' position.

Anna: Throughout, I've felt very supported by SLaM (Paul's team) and my friends, who are also my carers. I'm in a position where I can really accept the help from the various groups and bodies I have been directed towards that really help me. I am accompanied to medical appointments and had numerous home visits.

Eventually, the wheels set in motion for me to re-enter rehab – which is where I am now. It's looking good. I haven't been sober for so long (about six months now) for years, and I'm working towards a future that must be alcohol-free.

I couldn't have done it by myself. On reflection, I can't fault any of the care I've had. Staff (medical and otherwise) have been great; I just wasn't in a position to let it truly work for me.

My care in the community has been steadfast, supportive and kind. What can we learn from this? We must stick with the client, no matter how frustrating; the premise of 'you said....we did' is not always 'patient complains – team learns'; it sometimes is 'patient can't say.... team still tries to listen'.

I'm lucky, and I'm grateful that Paul's team operate in that way – thank you to all."

——————————————————-

"When we meet with someone who is feeling sad, empty, shaky or confused, we can quickly become convinced that something is wrong and that our role is to act urgently to fix them - to spin off into techniques, theories, and ideas to help them replace the actuality of their experience with what we believe they should be having instead. It's totally natural to want relief for those we care about and to do whatever we can to help; we don't need to pretend this isn't the case. We can hold that larger intention that they feel better while simultaneously staying open to a call emerging in the field between us into deeper territory.

Perhaps it is something more subtle, nuanced, and merciful than the relief they most long for. For the Friend, for a companion who will go with them into the dimly lit, endarkened landscape of the soul.

There is wisdom and guidance in the images, emotions, and somatic data arising into the relational field between ourselves and another, vital communication from the psyche serving an initiatory function beyond what we can perceive. We don't want to short-circuit that, mainly due to our anxiety and discomfort.

If we slow down and reflect, we might discover how much of our "fixing" activity, the movement toward relief, arises from an unresolved relationship with our own shadow, untended historic core vulnerabilities and complexes, and from the spinning of the ghosts of our unlived lives. It is possible that the most skilful and kind thing we can offer our friend is to sit in the carted energy with them, bearing witness to pure feeling together, in the claustrophobic or restless space, and stay near; to remove the burden that they come out of their experience, "feel better," or heal for us to stay close.

Perhaps they don't need to be healed but held, heard, felt and understood for someone to accompany them as the hidden wisdom unfolds.

Together, we can make sense of their experience and discover its meaning, crafting a safe and empathetic home where the shards of a broken world can reassemble."

<u>Matt Lica</u>[1]

---

1.   http://alovinghealingspace.blogspot.com/2022/03/

It wasn't until eight years later that I found a narrative in IFS that could explain what happened. My take is that from an IFS perspective when parts are in charge, there is disharmony as they have a singular (well-intended) perspective and an agenda that excludes other views.

On the other hand, when the Self is in the driving seat, there is no specific agenda but a space where all parts are welcomed and appreciated, allowing integration, connection, and inclusion. In this Self-process, details can be unburdened, which means releasing the emotions that part has been carrying or the parts felt able to move more into the background, allowing the Self to take the lead.

What could have occurred is that Anna reconnected with enough Self, which allowed her parts to reside more in the background, allowing her to choose a more wholesome (literally) direction in her life.

Speaking generally, addiction treatment has been mostly ineffective and successful discharges from treatment have been low if you take abstinence as a measure for completing treatment successfully.

It became evident for me that we are missing essential pieces of the puzzle, and I'm so grateful that the Polyvagal model and IFS have completed some of them.

So, over the years that I was working with people with addictions, I wanted to understand better what addiction is, and I became also interested in the question, "What is the opposite of addiction?"

From a medical perspective, the opposite of addiction is an allergy. Both sit on the extremes of the sliding scale. An allergy mobilises our immune system and attacks this identified intruder, the pathogen. It does not tolerate this pathogen. As a consequence, our body shows signs of being under attack.

Addiction, on the other hand, already starts with mobilising our system and looking for any way of relief in any way or form through consuming a drug or engaging in state-changing behaviour. The result is a (temporary) feeling of comfort, connection, purpose, quietness, feeling at peace or, as the opposite, being consumed by something.

From a physiological point of view, the opposite of addiction can be considered a natural state of rest.

At its core, addiction is linked with restlessness, the craving to find rest or relief by getting a "fix".

This "fix" can be considered to be a state change.

Being at "rest" is linked with our nervous system's ability to relax and be in a state of calmness and ease, connected and in balance.

Exposure to overwhelming experiences, specifically before age 18, affects our physiology. In the absence of an empathic witness who might have been able to support with co-regulating the nervous system and offering support in integrating that experience somewhat, the ACE study[2] (adverse childhood experiences) shows that overwhelming experiences before age 18 increase the occurrence of using coping mechanisms like substance use.

---

2.   http://www.connectbg.org/aces.html

From a society's perspective, Dr Vincent Felitti[3] reported that ACEs are "the leading determinant of what happens to the health of a nation's population".

<u>Polarisation</u>

The topic of addiction can bring about strong feelings and positions. Opinions can quickly polarise to the extent that they invite conflict, or people stop listening and distance themselves from others with different perspectives.

Familiarising yourself with polarised perspectives and becoming curious about their intention can create more space, allowing you to consider both polarities and find the positive qualities that those positions bring.

According to Beena Sharma[4] "Integrating Polarities is designed to help you supplement an "either/or" mentality with a flexible "both/and" mentality that is capable of bringing vastly different and divergent views together into a more complete vision of health and wholeness. And perhaps more importantly, it helps you to take the next step — to focus upon skillful and strategic actions that can help alleviate suffering and produce a more beneficial outcome".

Here is an example:

The duality matrix shows the polarities that we use when we make decisions. The 2 top squares show the value of both approaches, as you can see in the squares.

The two bottom squares show the negative values when too much emphasis is given to the approach above.

This will be the expected dynamic pattern:

---

3.   https://attachmentdisorderhealing.com/the-greatest-study-never-told/

4.   https://integrallife.com/integrating-polarities-training/

Going from the top left quadrant to the bottom left quadrant - when you pursue this line of management to long / overextend its functionality, going from the top right quadrant to the bottom right quadrant where again the adverse effects of a model will occur when you pursue this too long. Notice how the top left has opposite qualities compared to the bottom right quadrant.

Example: *symptom* vs *cause* management

	POSITIVE	
	cheap short term	long term savings
	low level training	effective
	large scaleablility	meaningful
	quick	healing
	crisis management	supports independance
	recovery	high exit from treatment
	SYMPTOM MANAGEMENT	**CAUSE MANAGEMENT**
	poor effectiveness	results take time
	creates dependance	individual
	no relief	expensive
	relapses	high training level
	return to treatment	
	low exit from treatment	

(Left vertical label top: POSITIVE; bottom: NEGATIVE)

Using the duality matrix is important because it prevents getting stuck in one perspective and allows one to tap into different perspectives, which validates that a view is a process - constantly calibrating against desired outcomes and experiences in real life. When a polarity is embraced without its' opposite, conflict is guaranteed. Using IFS language that considers both polarities is a capacity of the Self, whereas choosing one polarity as your perspective is a capacity of a part.

A whole-body recovery process from addiction means that you're not trying to manage your addiction but integrate factors that contributed to or caused your addiction.

Management processes are, generally speaking, top-down processes. In contrast, integration is a bottom-up process including full body sensing, incorporating our internal landscape, and registering "What is going on inside?".

Resources that you can tap into:

- ❖ Nurturing touch/bodywork sessions
- ❖ Movement
- ❖ Music
- ❖ Drawing
- ❖ Visualising / Imagining
- ❖ etc.

Three explorations that can help you orientate:

1. What am I aware of in this moment?

- Checking to see if you can stop/slow down, tune in, listen
- Are you holding your breath when you get some bad

news? - how is your breathing now?

- Do you notice stress in your body? Do you feel your heartbeat? Experience shallow breathing?
- What is your relationship with your body at this moment? Do you consider your body your friend, foe, or something else?

See if you can take a moment to take a baseline sensory snapshot of where you are now... yes ;-), this moment.

2. Are you able to be nourishing, grounding, and filling? You can do this when you:

❖ Turn focus inward

❖ Invite Curiosity

❖ Have no judgemental attitude

❖ Be open-hearted

❖ Permit yourself to experiment

❖ Go at your own pace

❖ Allow yourself to feel what you feel

❖ Shift attention from your mind to your body

❖ Enjoy the process

3. Healing internal resistance

This can be the background position that has coloured your life experiences, and that is hard to objectify as it is so much part of who you experience yourself to be.

One question that points to this fundamental relationship to life is: "Who is in control?"; "Who is driving the bus?"

Can the driver drive in the set-out direction with a sense of peace? Or is the driver struggling and finding life a constant battle that must be conquered, controlled and battled with?

Some qualities can give you a clue about who is driving the car: What is your capacity for humility, confidence, self-awareness, vulnerability, compassion, and discernment ...?

This being said ... there are also cultural and generational factors at play that influence our ability to navigate our way through life.

Being brought up in the Netherlands, over time, there has been a growing awareness of the country's role in the past as a coloniser and the harm it created.

Only a few years ago, I became aware that I grew up with privileges, which I became extra aware of by reading" My Grandmother's Hands" by Resmaa Menakem.

The writer made me aware of the horrific history of racialised trauma that has shaped our history in the West and culture and the role privileged people played at the expense of marginalised people.

This has led me to accept an invite to be part of a time-capsule project called "The Living Justice Project[5]", which is a collaborative, ethnographic project addressing the central question: What does it look, sound, and feel like to live (towards) justice in everyday *life?*

---

5.   http://www.livingjusticeproject.com/

3. TRAUMA-INFORMED CARE

Trauma-informed: awareness of the existence and impact of trauma.

Initially, the word trauma meant "wound" and referred to a physical condition. Now, the word trauma is also used in a psychological context to describe the challenging emotional consequences that living through a distressing event can have for an individual. Trauma can be described as a chronic disruption in connectedness (Porges).

In that context, trauma refers to what happens inside (related to the nervous system) of the client, not what happens (the event) to the client.

Traumatic events are challenging to define because the same event may be more traumatic for some people than others.

Distinctions used of trauma types:

❖ Acute, i.e. car crash
❖ Chronic, i.e. ongoing child abuse/war
❖ Complex, a combination of acute and chronic

Whether the event leaves a traumatic imprint depends on many factors in play. These factors are not only individual factors.

Our environment (stable-supportive-chaotic?) also affects our nervous system, and many other factors influence the degree of dis-regulation of our nervous system, for example:

- ❖ ability to be authentic
- ❖ attachment history
- ❖ support availability
- ❖ level of mindfulness
- ❖ ability for self-regulation
- ❖ neurological sensitivity
- ❖ exposure to collective trauma
- ❖ capacity for grounding

Scotland has been at the forefront of making trauma a national theme concerning everyone. They developed trauma training resources through the National Trauma Training Program[1] that are freely available to support all members of the Scottish workforce to meet their vision of:

"A trauma-informed and responsive nation and workforce that is capable of recognising where people are affected by trauma and adversity, that can respond in ways that prevent further harm and support recovery, and can address inequalities and improve life chances."

Scotland's position is that trauma is everyone's business, and every member of the Scottish Workforce has a role to play in understanding and responding to people

affected by trauma).

---

1.   https://www.traumatransformation.scot/

Four Levels

In Scotland, they make a distinction between 4 levels of trauma-informed care:

❖ Trauma-informed: for all members of the workforce, whether paid or unpaid.

❖ Trauma-skilled: for workers who are likely to be coming into contact with people who may have been affected by trauma.

❖ Trauma-enhanced: for workers who have a specific remit to respond to people known to be affected by trauma and are required to provide advocacy support or interventions or are required to adapt the way they work to take into account trauma reactions to do their job well and reduce risk of re-traumatisation.

❖ Trauma-specialist: for workers who have a specific remit to provide specialist interventions or therapies for people known to be affected by trauma with complex needs.

In this book, I combine levels 1 & 2 and consider them trauma-informed, as in addictions, a minimum of level 2 is required due to the complexity and prevalence (> 50%) of people who have trauma and addiction.

Levels 3 and 4 I consider trauma-integrated as this refers to a more subjective experience in addition to an objective understanding of what trauma is and how it can be addressed in the process of addiction recovery and healing.

As discussed earlier in Chapter 2, addiction can be considered a nervous system reaction dealing with unsettling experiences that challenge our sense of safety and trust and activate our trauma loop of sympathetic and dorsal vagal stuckness.

This is a way to numb or change our state and feelings of unsafety and mistrust by numbing or activating our physiology to prevent experiencing or feeling unsafe and unsettled. This strategy is an expression of the body's sympathetic flight response.

For feelings of safety and trust to disappear or to diminish significantly, especially for someone who grew up in an environment that does not give us a sense of security or belief in ourselves that was needed, emotionally, our culture can be traumatising.

Generally speaking, in our culture and childhood, we are not encouraged or invited to explore our emotional landscapes from a place of curiosity, interest, or empowerment.

In our capitalistic society, emotions are generally contextualised as a way of manipulation to sell products or catch someone's attention or as an experience that challenges the dominant mode of thinking and deciding in the West, rationality.

See an example of a trauma circle. It starts with daily triggers, leading to overwhelm, reactivity, and feeling uncomfortable, which leads, if not sufficient support or resilience is present, to increasing activation requiring more restriction.

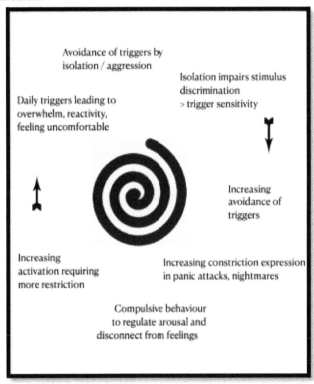

Avoidance of triggers by isolation / aggression

Isolation impairs stimulus discrimination
> trigger sensitivity

Daily triggers leading to overwhelm, reactivity, feeling uncomfortable

Increasing avoidance of triggers

Increasing activation requiring more restriction

Increasing constriction expression in panic attacks, nightmares

Compulsive behaviour to regulate arousal and disconnect from feelings

Culture

The ratio was declared the essence of what it means to be human by Descartes ("I think therefore I am"), and emotions were considered more primitive to the point that in England, it was considered a sign of distinction not to show any feelings at all (the famous "stiff upper lip").

Also, from the East, where the notion of Enlightenment was slowly exported to the West, being in a state of non-reactivity and non-emotionality was portrayed as a human's ultimate goal and purpose. Their message was "We are not our emotions", which became misunderstood and interpreted in the context that emotions need to be "transcended" to reach enlightenment.

My understanding that brought us to our current mistrust towards emotions is the observation that atrocities that we have endured and sometimes taken part in throughout the ages can be re-traumatising and experienced as overwhelming when accepted and considered with compassion and humility. Our Western culture does not promote or accept these reflections easily, so one might not want to or feel courageous enough to acknowledge them.

But this heritage shaped us, our nervous system, and our conditionings, amongst other things. Having had our nervous system so violated throughout history and trampled upon in periods where there was hardship, dictatorship, poverty, war, famine and poor knowledge of how to make sense of it all, it is not surprising to me that our emotions were considered more of a burden than a resource or an expression of important information and wisdom.

So, from this broader perspective, trauma can be considered an individual experience and a collective one. Collective trauma is a topic that, finally, is recognised and spoken about more and more.

Wikipedia[1] describes collective trauma as: "...psychological reactions to a traumatic event that affect[s] an entire society. Collective trauma represents a historical fact or event and a collective memory of a horrific event that happened to that group of people."

Examples of collective trauma are racism, slavery, the holocaust, and pandemics ... and these experiences can have set themselves in our body in the form of contractions or in the form of being sensitive in discussing these topics as feelings of shame and guilt can be linked with them.

In the absence of an environment, a social network, or a safe community where one can process the emotions and impact that those collective trauma experiences bring about and especially the feeling of powerlessness that accompanies this, it makes sense to focus on activities that give us a sense of control and distraction from these difficult emotions.

And yet, this is the way forward. This is what shadow dancing also proposes ... going through and coming to terms with the complex emotions and our burdened history.

Learning new somatic modalities like the Kiloby Inquiries[2] and Embodied Processing[3] taught me and permitted me to explore feelings and emotions in my body. This made me

---

1.   https://en.wikipedia.org/wiki/Collective_trauma

curious about how an emotion felt, where it showed itself, where it became present in my body, and any qualities (colour, shape, size, etc.) or properties (sticky, warm, fuzzy, etc.) of the emotion that would arise.

My capacity to witness my feelings and bodily sensations became more developed.

I developed an interest in associations that might be attached to the felt emotion, like ... images, words or other sensations that are linked somehow with the upcoming felt emotion. I learned to consider emotions as a source of information, data that can tell me about something or someone or arose to be felt and let go of in the process.

My ongoing journey is to keep welcoming and inviting emotions, feel them, and move with them in a connected, curious, and integrative way.

Especially "heavy" emotions like feeling weighted under stories of trauma shared by clients and considering what some clients had to go through, their upbringing and challenges, some successful and others not fortunate enough to re-tell the tale.

For me, leaning in emotions is challenging as I can sense my reactive pull not to go there, to numb myself or instead find some distractions.

The feeling wheel by Gloria Willcox clarifies the different shades of emotions coming from the six core emotions:

Sad - Mad - Scared - Joyful - Powerful - Peaceful.

---

2. https://kiloby.com/

3. https://www.thecentreforhealing.com/

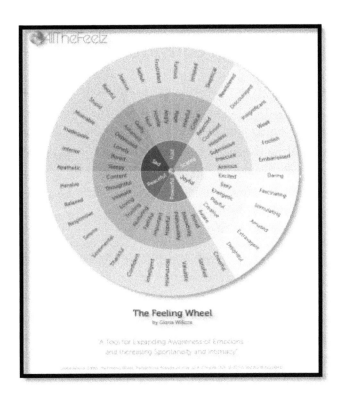

The Feeling Wheel
by Gloria Willcox

"A Tool for Expanding Awareness of Emotions
and Increasing Spontaneity and Intimacy"

68

Design considerations

For addiction services, which are focused on being risk-averse, the clinical environment is usually designed to be sterile, with functional objects in the room, alarm buttons, educational posters stating the risks of certain behaviours (stop smoking), etc.

For our nervous system, there will usually be more cues of danger to process than of safety, which can activate the sympathetic nervous system to fight or flight.

Being safer does not necessarily make us feel safer. Many of our social systems are focused on the features of danger, yet we have a profound sensitivity to safety features, and exposure to these can foster resilience.

This affects the ability to process information and reduces a sense of connection and safety.

Stephen Porges named four clinically relevant areas related to the nervous system:

1. Physiological state (reactive, expressive, present) influences how people respond to the world: intention, people behaviours, defensive mode .... can distort social awareness ...

2. Prosody voice, body posture, intentionality (biological movement), gesture, vocal expression

3. Low-frequency noise (elevator, machines, traffic noise): how you design your therapeutic setting (carpeting, wall hangings)

4. You must respect the vulnerability of the other person's nervous system. Their neuroception might not be the same as yours.

Here are other elements to consider in creating an environment and designing an addiction treatment program:

Environment considerations:

❖ Welcoming colours, noise (no low-frequency sounds, traffic, building work), sound, quality furniture, space, plants, shapes, safety, available information ...

❖ Friendly and empathic staff: managing/overview expectations, re-assuring, info about services in writing, support numbers, taking time to communicate, access to peer support.

Treatment program consideration:

1. *Safety*

Goal: assessment and physiological stabilisation
This can include:

❖ physical safety
❖ intake (4 weeks)
❖ initiation of medication-assisted therapy (MAT)
❖ environment safety

- ❖ ACE (adverse child experiences) study inquiry
- ❖ psychological/physical history
- ❖ "What happened ?" instead focus on problems

2. *Stabilisation*
Goal: overcoming emotional dysregulation

- ❖ Emotional stability
- ❖ Stabilising MAT dosing
- ❖ Aces + impact trauma education
- ❖ The Window of Tolerance model
- ❖ Relationship with body: neurofeedback
- ❖ Breathing practices
- ❖ Stigma exploration
- ❖ Support numbers / drop-in options
- ❖ Focus on agency and communion

3. *Recovery*
Goal: exploration and emotional regulation

- ❖ Widening "window of tolerance" development
- ❖ Reducing / evaluation MAT dosing
- ❖ Trauma therapy: exploring the legacy of trauma
- ❖ Art therapy, Assertiveness skills training
- ❖ DBT tools, effects of medication + side effects
- ❖ Focus on communion

4. *Healing / Embodied Recovery*
Goal: integration using embodied practices.

- ❖ Purpose & Meaning
- ❖ Decreasing shame and self-alienation
- ❖ Self-identity, Focus on agency
- ❖ Trauma as a memory in the past
- ❖ Social engagement
- ❖ Survivors, not victims' identification
- ❖ Creating connections in the community

4. TRAUMA-INTEGRATED CARE

By trauma-integrated, I refer to meeting the original trauma or the legacy (shadow) of our trauma in our experience.

This is a first-person subjective embodied activity.

Robert Kegan[1], a developmental psychologist at Harvard, has said that growth to a new stage happens when "the subject of one stage becomes the object of the subject at the next stage."

This is the distinction between subject and object:

"Subject" is something I identify with and experience as "me." "Object" is something I experience as "not me."

"Subject" is something I can only take a 1st person ("I") perspective on. "Object" is something I take a 3rd person ("it") perspective on. In other words, I can stand back from it and view it objectively.

One defence to experiencing overwhelm is splitting off what we experience and feel and changing a 1st person's subjective experience into a 3rd person's object (I can't accept this and alienate this experience as something other than me).

Integrating these previously split-off experiences or feelings can start by becoming curious and feeling safe enough to reconnect with them gradually (allow that part to be recognised and welcomed as a subjective experience, a part of me that I experienced).

---

1.   https://medium.com/@NataliMorad/how-to-be-an-adult-kegans-theory-of-adult-development-d63f4311b553

Different Models

Several models point to a process and a shift where the balance of a partial (split-off) view shifts to a holistic perspective.

Integral Model

One of these models is the Integral Theory[1] by Ken Wilber, as discussed in Chapter 2, and you can find a summary in the Appendix.

Integral theory is a school of philosophy that seeks to integrate all of human wisdom into a new, emergent worldview that can accommodate the gifts of all previous worldviews, including those which have been historically at odds: science and religion, Eastern and Western schools of thought, and pre-modern, modern and post-modern worldviews. Integral theory builds on the foundations of evolutionary theory[2].

Ken Wilber describes a process of evolution with initial partial views where every successive view believes their view is the only correct view. He calls this Tier 1 until there is a shift to Tier 2, which allows for appreciation of previous levels of Tier 1 without the need for identification with one of those levels and with the appreciation that all Tier 1 levels have a (partial) truth to express.

Drama and Empowerment Triangle

---

1.   https://integrallife.com/

2.   https://www.dailyevolver.com/

Another model is the Drama Triangle[3], initially presented by Stephen Kaplan. This social interaction and conflict model was developed by psychologist Stephen Karpman in 1968. In this model, conflict is represented as a game in which there are three roles:

1. The Victim: The person who feels powerless, oppressed, and helpless.

2. The Rescuer: The person who intervenes, often without being asked, to help the victim.

3. The Persecutor: The person blaming, critical, oppressive, controlling, rigid, authoritative, angry, hostile, and superior.

The drama triangle illustrates how individuals alternate between these three roles, creating a cycle of drama and conflict. It's crucial to note that all these roles are dysfunctional and keep individuals trapped in destructive behaviour patterns.

The Empowerment Triangle is an alternative model in which the individuals play different roles that are much more beneficial and productive.

This model encourages personal accountability, empowerment, and constructive support. It replaces the negative behaviours associated with the Drama Triangle with positive replacements, promoting healthier interactions and relationships.

1. The Victim is allowed to become the Creator: Instead of feeling powerless, the Creator takes accountability for their decisions.

2. The Rescuer is allowed to become the Coach: The Coach assists the creator in coming up with solutions and new ideas instead of always trying to fix a situation.

---

3.   https://leadershiptribe.com/blog/the-drama-triangle-explained

3. The Persecutor is allowed to become the Challenger: The Challenger presents difficult situations to help stimulate growth instead of punishing or criticising.

Visual representation triangle transformation:

Drama Empowerment

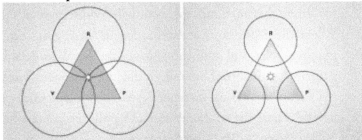

4

4.   http://www.therapywithalessio.com/

Internal Family Systems

A third model is Internal Family Systems.

IFS showed how we internalised similar roles of the drama triangle: the manager, firefighter and exile and developed these parts to protect the Self.

These dysfunctional roles burdened those part positions. When these positions are unburdened, these parts can give up their roles and transition under the Self's leadership to situations similar to the details of the Empowerment Triangle.

A container visual metaphor (see following picture) can be helpful where the container stands for all that you are, which we'll represent as 100% before treatment.

Self-manifestation might be limited due to trauma and parts expression. After treatment, Self-expression could have increased as trauma resided and parts retreated more into the background.

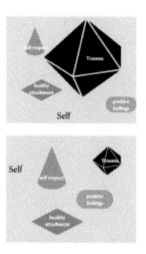

Qualities of the Self are, for example, clarity, confidence, courage, calmness, curiosity, connectedness, creativity, compassion, and choice.

This balance is related to the danger/safety equation as described by Deb Dana, where when cues of safety outweigh the cues of danger, there is readiness for connection and new stories emerge, change is possible, and there is a quality of wellbeing.

When cues of danger outweigh the cues of safety, there is an activation of survival responses, stuckness in a story, little room for change and a sense of dis-ease.

One of the most critical areas where addiction services can advance is to develop training and clarity to the drama triangle dynamic, explore these positions, and allow them to transform into more integrated parts.

Dual Attention

A key healing dynamic in trauma treatment should be developing our ability for dual attention. Dan Siegel calls this in his book "The Developing Mind[1]" the integration of consciousness. An example would be to ask if someone is aware of their inner observing, compassionate voice (similar to the Self in the IFS model).

Dual attention indicates our ability to hold two perspectives simultaneously and in context. For example, we can be aware of the object we are looking at and be mindful that we are looking.

An example of dual attention in dealing with trauma is that we can develop an awareness of being triggered in a situation and, at the same time, experience an increasing level of self-regulation.

That is a first step. We can then choose to adequately respond in a way that allows us to stay emotionally regulated and reduce dysregulation.

In the context of trauma, dual attention can enable us to be aware of the part that is affected by the trauma while allowing for and mobilising support for that part. This is remarkable; I consider this a superpower.

I have heard of a situation where a client seemed very distressed. Still, as she was with a therapist and had access to "Self" when asked, she mentioned she felt not overwhelmed as she had enough access to "Self" to feel safe and supported.

---

1. https://drdansiegel.com/book/the-developing-mind/

In IFS, there is a process to inquire into parts and to assess if there is enough Self-present to safely reconnect with the part and listen and be with what it has to communicate. This communication can be through words or images, physical sensations or movements.

Post-traumatic growth

Post-traumatic growth will not occur just by integrating trauma, reconnecting with parts in us that were disconnected and dampening the qualities that were attached to the disowned part, like narratives such as "I don't deserve to be happy" or "Something bad will happen".

What is also needed is the amplification, savouring and deepening of qualities from the ventral experience—savouring positive experiences.

The ventral experience can be nurtured in several ways. See if you can contemplate these questions and notice the quality of your experience:

❖ Can you remember a ventral moment in the past?

❖ Can you notice a ventral moment in the present?

❖ Can you anticipate a ventral moment in the future?

The ventral state, sympathetic state, and dorsal state can also blend between them. Jan Winhall describes these blended states in her book "Treating Trauma and Addiction with the Felt Sense Polyvagal Model", in which she provides a model of addiction informed by the Polyvagal Model combined with the practice of Focusing and the felt-sense model from Somatic Experiencing[1] by Eugene Gendlin.

Examples of blended states:

---

1.   https://www.somaticexperiencing.com/

❖ Play (Fun / Fired up) is an example of a blended state between ventral and sympathetic.

❖ Fixate / Freeze is a blended state between sympathetic and dorsal.

❖ Stillness (Flow) can be considered a blended state between ventral and dorsal.

There is so much more to explore and develop in the area of post-traumatic growth, especially from people with a lived experience, that this might deserve a separate future edition.

I wish to conclude with a quote from the book "Call Me By My True Names: The Collected Poems of Thich Hat Hanh," which, for me, points to the importance of nervous system regulation and how it affects our world.

"Earth will be safe when we feel in us enough safety"
Thich Nhat Hanh

APPENDIX

This Appendix is co-created with AI (Chat CPT-4) and contains summaries of the Integral Theory, the Polyvagal Model, the Internal Family System model and a link to examples of using "The Context".

Integral Theory: A Summary

Integral Theory, developed by Ken Wilber, is a comprehensive philosophical framework that seeks to integrate all theories and methodologies into a cohesive whole. It is a transdisciplinary approach to understanding human and universal dynamics and interactions.

Integral Theory entails four primary aspects, which are also referred to as the "four quadrants" or the "AQAL" model (All Quadrants, All Levels. All stages, All lines, All types). The four quadrants are I (Upper Left), We (Lower Left), It (Upper Right), and Its (Lower Right).

1. Upper Left (UL) "I": This quadrant represents an individual's subjective or internal world. It includes consciousness, emotions, cognition, experiences, and psychological aspects.

2. Lower Left (LL) "We": This quadrant encapsulates collective interior spaces, including shared meanings, cultures, and social and linguistic constructs. It's about how groups, communities, and societies define themselves and the expectations they create.

3. Upper Right (UR) "It": This is the objective exterior of an individual. In human terms, it includes observable actions and behaviours.

4. Lower Right (LR) "Its": This quadrant refers to the external collective or system. It comprises societal systems, environment, technology, infrastructure, and organisational structures.

Each of these quadrants is further divided into two zones, leading to the eight zones.

In the Upper Left, Zone #1 encompasses direct experiential awareness and immediate perception (phenomenology). Zone #2 focuses on introspection and psychological theories.

In the Upper Right, Zone #5 covers empirical observation, behaviourist accounts, and third-person investigations. Zone #6 involves a detailed functional analysis of individual units of a whole (like cells in a body).

In the Lower Left, Zone #3 is about shared understanding within a culture/group, interpreted through dialogue and mutual understanding. Zone #4 includes theories that analyse collective worldviews, cultural artefacts, and social hermeneutics.

In the Lower Right, Zone #7 is about observing systems and their modes of operation. Zone #8 involves the analysis of specific systems in their overall context and network.

Integral theory states that all of these quadrants and zones are important for a holistic understanding of the world, and it invites practitioners to consider perspectives from all areas.

A "holon" is a central concept in Ken Wilber's Integral Theory. The term, first coined by Arthur Koestler, denotes something that is simultaneously a whole and a part.

In Wilber's context, a holon refers to an entity that, at the same time, is an autonomous, self-contained individual (in relation to its sub-parts) and a dependent part of a larger system (or a greater whole).

Every holon has a dual tendency: a drive towards preserving its individuality as a whole and a drive towards functioning as a part of a larger system. Wilber refers to these as the "agency" (self-assertion, self-preservation) and "communion" (cooperation, integration with the collective), respectively.

Furthermore, Wilber outlines four fundamental capacities of every holon, known as the 'Four Faces of Every Holon':

1. Agency: The capacity to resist the environment and maintain individuality.

2. Communion: The capacity to merge and blend with the environment.

3. Self-transcendence: The ability to evolve and become part of larger, more complex systems.

4. Self-Dissolution: The ability to break down and offer its components to create new entities.

While connecting holons, Wilber underscores that evolution takes a form of "nested hierarchies" or "holarchies", in which each subsequent level of development transcends but also includes its predecessors.

Every subsequent holon possesses depth (greater complexity, consciousness, or capacity) rather than just a breadth (greater span or quantity). This perspective offers a harmonious blend of individualism and collectivism—an integral vision.

The Polyvagal Model: A Summary

The human body is a profound and intricate machine that constantly alters its functioning in response to the environment around it. One of these fascinating responses is encapsulated in the Polyvagal Model, a revolutionary theory propounded by Dr. Stephen Porges.

Essentially, the Polyvagal Model explores how our bodies respond to varying degrees of safety and danger, predominantly regulated by the vagus nerve.

The vagus nerve, the longest cranial nerve in our body, touches nearly all our vital organs, influencing our heart rate, digestion, respiratory rate, and other crucial functions. It also plays a lead role in the Autonomic Nervous System, the body's automated control system.

Herein is where 'Polyvagal' derives its name, 'Poly' meaning many, and 'vagal' refers to the vagus nerve, indicating the nerve's multiple roles.

Understanding the Polyvagal Model entails unpacking three elemental systems represented in the Polyvagal Ladder. At the ladder's base, we have the dorsal vagal complex, the first and the oldest of the systems in evolution. This system is associated with immobilisation responses, like fainting or freezing when faced with a significant threat--colloquially said to be 'playing dead'. Responses such as feeling numb, disconnected, or shutting down emanate from this primitive system.

The sympathetic nervous system is the midway rung up the ladder, responsible for mobilisation. It prepares the body for a 'fight or flight' response by stimulating functions that prompt alertness and action. For instance, an increase in heart rate and blood pressure, suspension of digestion, and dilation of pupils all work in unison to equip us against perceived danger.

Lastly, the ventral vagal complex is at the peak of the ladder and is associated with social engagement, relaxation, and rejuvenation. This 'resting and digesting' system is activated when situations are deemed safe. It allows for social bonding, communication, creative thinking, and feelings of safety and contentment. Notably, these calming functions are believed to be facilitated by the vagus nerve.

However, humans do not statically exist in one of these states. We're continually fluctuating up and down the Polyvagal Ladder based on our perception of safety and environmental threats. Our daily interactions and experiences determine the rung we occupy at any moment.

The Polyvagal Model moves beyond merely classifying responses; it identifies the crucial 'neuroceptive' process – the unconscious sensing our nervous system engages in to gauge whether situations are safe, dangerous, or life-threatening. This underlines the understanding that our body's responses, particularly under stress, are inherently survival patterns rather than chosen behaviours.

Moreover, the Polyvagal Model brings a persuasive shift in mental health perspectives. It provides us with a physiological explanation for symptoms observed in trauma survivors and those with disorders like autism and anxiety. For instance, a trauma survivor, perceiving danger, may 'shut down' by activating the primitive dorsal vagal complex for self-preservation.

Internal Family Systems: A Summary

The Internal Family Systems (IFS) model, developed by Dr. Richard Schwartz in the 1980s, is an innovative and empowering approach to psychotherapy. Delving into the world of the subconscious, the IFS model offers a compassionate framework for understanding and nurturing our inner world. It holds a profound belief: the core self, inherently possessing qualities of compassion, curiosity, and calmness, is present in every individual.

The fundamental concept within the IFS model is that the human psyche is not a single entity but rather a composite of numerous sub-personalities or parts, each with distinctive characteristics and roles. According to this model, these parts fall into three categories: exiles, managers, and firefighters.

Exiles are the wounded and vulnerable parts of us that have experienced trauma or pain. Two types of protective parts shield us from their pain: managers and firefighters. Managers are proactive parts that aim to keep us in control of situations and prevent us from feeling pain by maintaining order and routine. Conversely, firefighters act reactively, engaging in impulsive behaviours to distract us when pain or trauma becomes immediate and overwhelming.

The brilliance of the Internal Family Systems model lies in its transformative approach that helps individuals build harmonious relationships with their parts. This process invites the empathetic qualities of the core self to comprehend and heal the pain that the parts carry. Rather than trying to change or eliminate these parts, IFS encourages us to welcome and understand each part, regardless of its role. Consequently, this model enables us to foster an inner dialogue and cultivate relationships amongst these parts, ultimately promoting internal balance and personal growth.

The IFS Model's uniqueness is reflected in its non-pathologizing view of mental health, where symptoms or issues are understood as parts stuck in extreme roles due to unresolved pain. This perspective infuses compassion into the therapy process, acknowledging every part's effort to protect the self.

The model has been applied extensively in various therapeutic settings. It has proven beneficial for individuals grappling with issues such as trauma, depression, anxiety, and eating disorders. Its application in couple and family therapy has also enabled positive outcomes, enhancing understanding and intimacy.

However, IFS is not a 'one-size-fits-all' solution like any model. It requires the individual to be open to exploring their past experiences and emotions, a journey that may not resonate with everyone. However, for those who engage with it, the IFS model offers potential pathways to understanding oneself more deeply.

To conclude, the Internal Family Systems model is a groundbreaking approach to psychotherapy, enabling individuals to navigate their inner landscape with compassion and understanding. By recognising our multifaceted psyche and cultivating relationships with each part, we can begin to heal, grow, and hold space for our authentic selves to thrive.

The Context

The Context merges AI with mental model visualisation to help executives, consultants, academics, analysts, and others map and understand the fuller dynamics driving their mission-critical contexts. These visualisations might not be our usual viewpoints, but they can give us new insights and perspectives on a situation we haven't considered.

I chose the following hypothetical context and challenge:

"Create a Social Sector Organisational Capacity Development Map for a charity supporting people impacted by drugs, alcohol and related issues using a timeline from 2024 to 2028 where they become trauma-informed in 1 year, trauma-skilled in 2 years and eventually trauma-integrated across the following developmental lines: Scope of Impact, Strategic Capacity, Organisational Structure, Funding Model, Partnership Model, Program Design Model, Core Values, Organisational Culture, Organization Learning Model, Staff Development Model, Pain points."

This link[1] brings you to the examples for this organisation to transition into trauma-informed and integrated service.

And for more information you can visit my website: https://www.pauldubuf.info/organisations

---

1.   https://www.pauldubuf.info/organisations

RESOURCES

- Stephen Porges; https://www.stephenporges.com/[1]
- Poly-vagal Theory; https://youtu.be/8AnHlx3qZ30[2]
- Books from: Gabor Mate, Janine Fisher, Bessel v/d Kolk, Dan Siegel, Deb Dana, Bruce Alexander
- Titration Explained[3]: Never rush trauma healing.

- Four ways to spark up our social engagement nervous system without socialising[4]

- Can I heal if I'm living in a toxic environment?[5]

- How to set healthy boundaries in a toxic relationship[6]

- Jan Winhall: Treating Trauma and Addiction with the Felt Sense Polyvagal Model

- Scotland's national trauma training program:

https://transformingpsychologicaltrauma.scot

- Trauma-Informed Care and Practice Organizational

---

1. https://youtu.be/ec3AUMDjtKQ?si=gYlbUefRn6KmQ3G5

2. https://www.youtube.com/watch?v=8AnHlx3qZ30&t=0s

3. https://youtu.be/Qxd8hTMUSOY

4. https://youtu.be/jDigX6uP89o

5. https://youtu.be/U4IgtrZDJXg

6. https://youtu.be/NGHD1cLKclM

Toolkit: https://mhcc.org.au/resource/

- SAMHSA's Concept of Trauma and Guidance for a Trauma-Informed Approach; https://ncsacw.acf.hhs.gov/userfiles/files/ SAMHSA_Trauma.pdf

About the Author

Paul graduated as a registered nurse in 1994. In the Netherlands and the UK, he worked within addiction services in prevention, treatment, aftercare, dual diagnosis, project management, training and innovation. He became a trauma-informed and somatic practitioner to support his clients more effectively. Paul focuses in his work on the relationship between trauma and addiction, the causes and legacy of trauma.

In addition to his work as a nurse prescriber, he offers consultancy for addiction organisations to transition and become trauma-informed and integrated.

In 2023, Paul was recognised by the International Council of Nurses for his work and received certification as a Global Nurse Consultant.

135

ABOUT THE AUTHOR

INDEX

A

ACE (adverse childhood experiences), 54
Action phase, 20
Acute, 60
Adolescent, 16
Aftermath, 45
Alcohol, 35, 37, 41, 47, 48, 50, 92
Amplification, 81
Appreciation, 20, 74
AQAL, 33, 84
Art therapy, 71

B

Biosphere, 22
Bleak, 48

C

Calibrating, 57
Cannabis, 39
Cause-Effect, 6, 7
Chaotic, 1, 60
Chess, 16
Chronic, 35-38, 60
Clinical Addictions Group (CAG), 47
Cocaine, 39
Cognitive techniques, 4
Co-morbidities, 37
Compassion, 59, 65, 78, 79, 90, 92
Compassionate, 3, 15, 19, 29, 79, 90
Complex, 6, 9, 17, 19, 33, 35, 44, 49, 60, 62, 66, 86-89

O

P

Q

R

S

T

V

W